G. THALBEN-BALL

LAUDATE DOMINUM

A COLLECTION OF INTROITS

BOOK I

NOVELLO

Cat. No. NOV 030103

CONTENTS

INTROITS

BOOK I

GEORGE THALBEN-BALL

1

2

3

Blessed be his glorious name for ever; and let the whole earth be filled with his glory, Amen, A - men.

4

O praise God in his holiness; praise him in the firmament of his power.

5

Thou, O Lord, hast made us for thy - self, and our

till _dim._   ten. pp

hearts   are   rest - less   till they rest   in   thee.

dim.   pp

6

O   Lord,   thou hast   search-ed me   out and   known   me:

whi - ther shall I   go   then   from thy   pres - ence?

7

The Lord is gra - cious and mer - ci - ful, slow   to

an-ger,and of great good-ness. His mer-cy is o-ver all   his works.

4

8

Here - in is love, not that we loved God,___ but that___ he___ loved___ us. Here - in is love.

9

In the be - ginn - ing was the Word:___ and the Word was made___ flesh and dwelt a - mong___ us: and we be - held his___ glo - ry, full of grace and___ truth.

10

Copyright, 1954, by Novello & Company, Limited

11

Copyright, 1954, by Novello & Company, Limited

12

6

me: and bring me un-to thy ho-ly hill and to thy dwell-ing.

13

This is my com-mand-ment, that ye

love to-geth-er as I have lov-ed you.

14

Draw nigh to God, and he will draw nigh to you.

15

Freely

Be-hold the Cross dis-played, where-on the Sa-viour of the world did

hang. O come ye, O come ye, let us wor-ship and bow____ down.

16

If an-y man will fol-low me, let him for-sake him-

self and take up his____ cross and fol - low me. Who-so-

ev - er shall en -dure un-to the end, he shall be____ saved.

17

Thou, O Lord, O Lord, art in the midst of us and we are called by thy name.

8

20

21

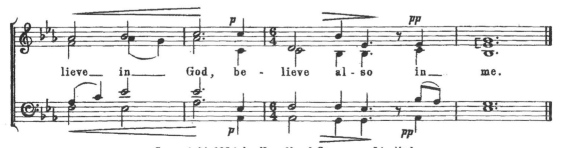

22

23

24

25

26

, rall.
p dim.

come,— O come— let us— a-dore him. Al-le-lu - ia.

pp

To H. W. D.

27

♩ = 84
pp

Ye are the tem-ple of God, and the Spi-rit of God dwell-eth in you.

pp

28

♩ = 66
p

rall.   a tempo   pp

As ma-ny as are led by the Spi-rit of God, they are the sons of— God.

p   pp

To G. D.

29

Allegro ♩ = 104
f

rall.

Praise the Lord O my soul, and all— that is with-in me praise his ho - ly name.

f

30

Flowing, in free rhythm
p

The Lord our God hath shewn us his glo - ry. O come, let

p

us — a - dore — him, let us a - dore — him.

31

Like as a fa - ther pi - ti - eth his own chil - dren,

ev - en so is the Lord — mer - ci - ful un - to them that fear — him.

32

Je - sus said, Fear not; your Fa - ther know - eth what things ye have need of

be - fore you ask him. Ask, and it shall be giv - en you; Seek, and

ye shall find; knock, and it shall be o - pen'd un - to you.

33

The hour com - eth, and now it is, when true wor - ship -

pers shall wor - ship the Fa - ther in spi - rit and in truth.

34

Give the Lord the hon-our due ___ un - to his name: wor-ship the Lord with

ho - ly wor-ship. A - men, A - men.